PIERRE RODE

TWENTY-FOUR CAPRICES

(STUDIES)

For the

VIOLIN

In the

24 MAJOR AND MINOR SCALES

Edited and Fingered by

FERDINAND DAVID

Published in 2019 by Allegro Editions

24 Caprices for Violin
ISBN: 978-1-9748-9994-4 (paperback)

Cover design by Kaitlyn Whitaker

Cover image: "Music Sheet" by danielo courtesy of
Shutterstock; "Violin Front View Isolated on White"
by AGCuesta courtesy of Shutterstock

ALLEGRO
EDITIONS

Caprices.

Down - bow ⊓.
Up - bow V.
Positions I, II, III, IV, V, VI, VII.

E means "on the E string."
A   „   „   „ A   „
D   „   „   „ D   „
G   „   „   „ G   „

PIERRE RODE.

strongly mark the staccato notes.

This study should be played in the second position.

Commodo. ($\quad$ = 120)

3.

dolce legato.

hold down 2nd finger.

10

14

16

18

This study is to be played in the fourth position.

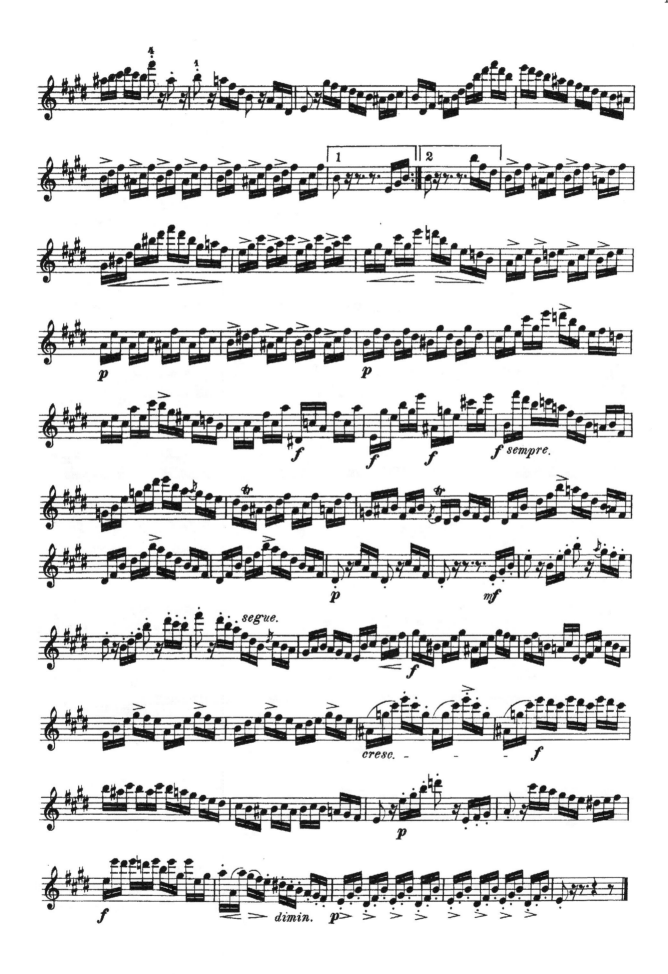

This study is to be played in the third position.

22

25

do not take too long bows.

32

f e sostenuto.

36

44

48